THE
WINNIE-THE-POOH
BABY
BOOK

*With texts by A.A.Milne
and original illustrations
by E.H. Shepard*

METHUEN CHILDREN'S BOOKS

'Hush!' said Christopher Robin,
turning round to Pooh.
'Hush!' said Pooh, turning round
quickly to Piglet.
'Hush!' said Piglet to Kanga.
'Hush!' said Kanga to Owl,
while Roo said 'Hush!'
several times to himself
very quietly.

In which we are introduced to

THE NEW BABY

Son/Daughter _____

Born to _____

Date _____

Time _____

Place _____

Weight _____

When I first heard his name, I said, just as
you are going to say, 'But I thought he was a boy?'
  'So did I,' said Christopher Robin.
  'Then you can't call him Winnie?'
  'I don't. He's Winnie-ther-Pooh.
Don't you know what "*ther*" means?'

NAMING THE NEW BABY

Full name _____

Registered at _____

Christened at _____

Godmother _____

Godfather _____

FIRST VISITORS

Your visitors can sign this page

Outside his house Pooh found Piglet, jumping up and down trying to reach the knocker.

'Hallo, Piglet,' he said.

'Hallo, Pooh,' said Piglet.

'What are *you* trying to do?'

'I was trying to reach the knocker,' said Piglet. 'I just came round –'

'Let me do it for you,' said Pooh kindly. So he reached up and knocked at the door.

Piglet had gone back to his own
house to get Eeyore's balloon, and he
ran as fast as he could so as to get to
Eeyore before Pooh did; for he thought
that he would like to be the first
one to give a present.

And running along, and thinking
how pleased Eeyore would be,
he didn't look where he was going…

He gave Eeyore the small piece of damp rag.
  'Is this it?' said Eeyore, a little surprised.
Piglet nodded.
  'My present?'
Piglet nodded again.
  'Thank you, Piglet,' said Eeyore. 'You don't
mind my asking,' he went on, 'but what colour
was this balloon when it – when it *was* a
balloon?'

FIRST GIFTS AND CARDS

Gift/Card ——————————   Gift/Card ——————————

From ————————————   From ————————————

Gift/Card ——————————   Gift/Card ——————————

From ————————————   From ————————————

Gift/Card ——————————   Gift/Card ——————————

From ————————————   From ————————————

The Piglet lived in a very grand house in the middle of a beech-tree. Next to his house was a piece of broken board which had: 'TRESPASSERS W' on it. He said it was his grandfather's name, and had been in the family for a long time. Christopher Robin said you *couldn't* be called Trespassers W, and Piglet said yes, you could, because his grandfather was, and it was short for Trespassers Will, which was short for Trespassers William.

THE FAMILY TREE

Mother _____   Father _____

Grandmother _____   Grandmother _____

Grandfather _____   Grandfather _____

Brothers and Sisters _____

_____

The Family Home _____

_____

Kanga and Roo were spending a quiet afternoon in a sandy part of the Forest. Baby Roo was practising very small jumps in the sand, and falling down mouse-holes and climbing out of them, and Kanga was fidgeting about and saying 'Just one more jump, dear, and then we must go home.' And at that moment who should come stumping up the hill but Pooh.

'Look at me jumping,' squeaked Roo, and fell into another mouse-hole.

FIRST EVENTS

Very first smile _____

First laugh _____

First rolled over _____

Sat up _____

Crawled _____

Stood up _____

First steps _____

First walked _____

First pair of shoes _____

First tooth _____

First hair cut _____

First words _____

_____

_____

WEIGHT

At Birth _____

1 week _____

2 weeks _____

3 weeks _____

1 month _____

3 months _____

6 months _____

9 months _____

At 1 year _____

Pooh put a large honey-pot on the cloth and they sat down to breakfast. Tigger took a large mouthful of honey . . . and he looked up at the ceiling with his head on one side, and made exploring noises with his tongue, and considering noises, and what-have-we-got-*here* noises . . . and then he said in a very decided voice:

'Tiggers don't like honey.'

FIRST FOOD

Weaned ————————————

First tastes ————————————

First food ————————————

First finger foods ————————————

Favourite food ————————————

————————————

————————————

————————————

Well, he was humming a hum to himself, and walking gaily along, when suddenly he came to a sandy bank, and in the bank was a large hole.

'Aha!' said Pooh. 'If I know anything about anything, that hole means Rabbit, and Rabbit means Company, and Company means Food and Listening-to-Me-Humming and such like. *Rum-tum-tum-tiddle-um.*'

So he bent down, put his head into the hole, and called out: 'Is anybody at home?'

THE FIRST OUTINGS
AND VISITS

Place —————————————— Place ——————————————

Date —————————————— Date ——————————————

Visited —————————————— Visited ——————————————

Date —————————————— Date ——————————————

   'We are all going on an Expedition,' said
Christopher Robin.
   'Going on an Expotition?' said Pooh eagerly.
'I don't think I've ever been on one of those.
Where are we going to on this Expotition?'
   'Expedition, silly old Bear. It's got an "x" in it.'
   'Oh!' said Pooh. 'I know.' But he didn't really.
   'We're going to discover the North Pole.'
   'Oh!' said Pooh again. 'What *is* the North Pole?'

THE FIRST HOLIDAY

Place/Date _____

Events _____

THE FIRST CHRISTMAS

Place _____

Visitors _____

Presents _____

'This party,' said Christopher Robin, 'is a party because of what someone did, and we all know who it was, and it's his party, because of what he did, and I've got a present for him and here it is.' Then he felt about a little and whispered, 'Where is it?'

FIRST BIRTHDAY

Party day _____

Guests _____

Cards from _____

Presents from _____

FIRST PHOTOGRAPHS

FIRST PHOTOGRAPHS